Seek and Find

Akaloo 2
PreK-K

by Debbie Trafton O'Neal

Illustrated by
Constanza Bassaluzo
Alessia Girasole
Dana C. Regan

All night and day God led the way,
Through the desert and the Red Sea,
With fire and clouds God went ahead
To keep the people free.

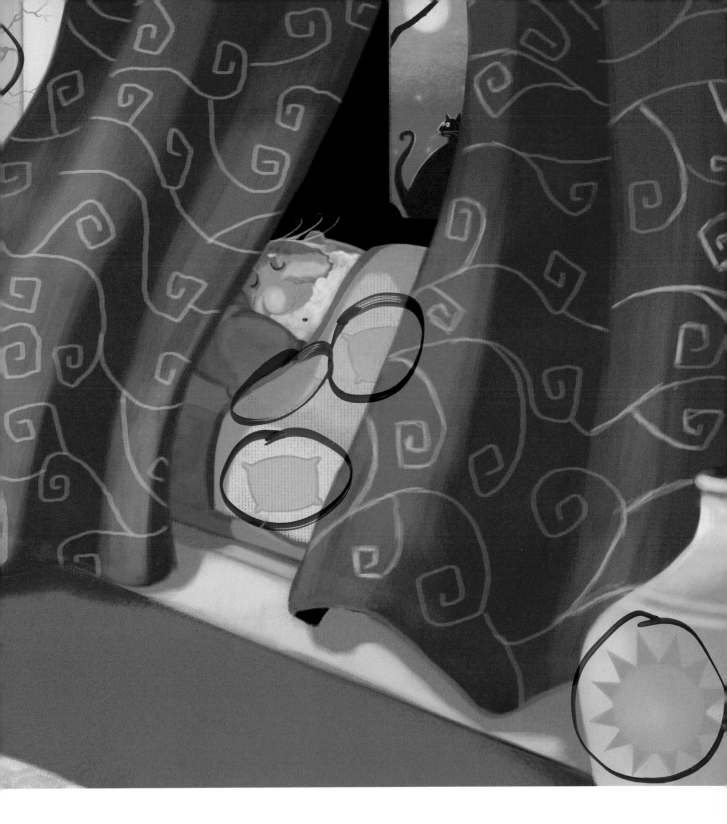

s a dark and quiet night
Samuel went to bed;
someone called out "Samuel!"
e got up instead.
you call me, Eli? Here I am," said he.

But God was calling Samuel,
It happened one, two, three.
Eli said to listen, to hear what God would say,
So Samuel said, "I'm listening!" when God
    called him that day.

Follow the star,
Said the three.
Where is Jesus?
Look and see!

Jesus was missing! Where could he be?
Mary and Joseph went looking to see.
Hurrah! They found him.
Can you find him too?
Look in the temple
To see if you do.

9

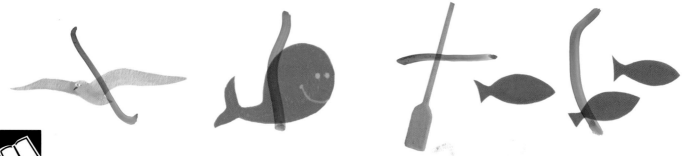

It was dark and stormy and the wind began to blow
In the boat, fast asleep, Jesus didn't know.
"Wake up, wake up!" the disciples said. "We are afraid this night!"
Then Jesus calmed the wind and waves and everything was quiet.

BIBLE 5

Five brown loaves, two silver fish,
One small boy who shared,
More than all of them could eat
From someone small who cared.

13

BIBLE 6

One brown donkey,
Jesus the king.
Hosanna! Hosanna!
Hear children sing.

Three friends worked together
Making their tents
Telling all about Jesus
Wherever they went.

17

GOD 1

God's people were hungry,
God promised them food;
They ate bread from heaven
And it tasted good!

Daniel loved God
He prayed every day,
God kept Daniel safe
And the lions away.

GOD 2

I say things I shouldn't say
And do things I shouldn't do,
But God forgives me anyway,
And God forgives you too!

GOD 3

From dark to light
From night to day
God always listens
When I pray!

25

GOD 4

A cat, a dog, a spotted bug
Apples in a tree,
God blesses us with all the world
All gifts for you and me.

Come one, come all
Come and see
The fun we have
Jesus and me!

29

Look in the church!
What do you see?
So many smiling faces.
Can you count more than three?

Church or home
Night or day
God is listening
When I pray.

God loves me
I love God too,
I share love
By things I do!

Pick up my toys
Feed my fish
Set the table
Dry a dish.

I am helpful
You are too!
What are helpful
　things you do?

It's time to get ready
To worship and pray,
Because it is Sunday,
God's special day!

CHURCH 2

Here is my church
Here is the steeple
When you go inside
You'll see all the people!

Splish, splash, splish, splash!
Water washing me,
Reminding me always
That God loves me!

Look up at the altar
See the bread and wine;
Remembering forgiveness
That God's love is mine.

CHURCH 5

Up on the wall there is a cross
For everyone to see,
A reminder of Lord Jesus
Who died for you and me.

Seniors

CHURCH 6

Tables and chairs
Cookies and punch
People laughing and talking
Fun for a bunch!

Look in a mirror
What can you view?
One of God's children,
Yes, it's you!

I love my parents
My parents love me
We're part of God's family
It's easy to see!

All around God's world
Are kids like me and you,
Sharing with each other
In all we say and do.

55

WORLD 2

To say that I forgive you
When I am feeling mad,
Isn't always easy
But always makes me glad!

It makes God happy when I pray
My fingers folded tight
God always hears me when I pray
Any day or night.

Look around the world God made
What funny things to see!
We add our smiles and laughter
God's gifts for you and me.

WORLD 5

w.akaloo.org

Seek and Find

Can you find the following
hidden pictures in this book?

 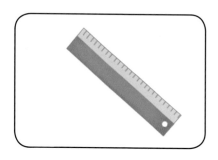 

  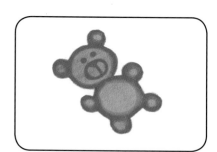

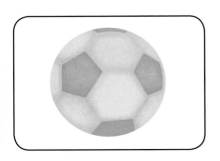 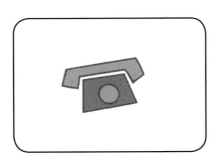 

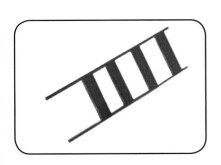 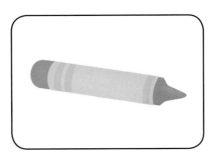 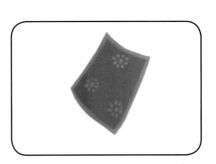

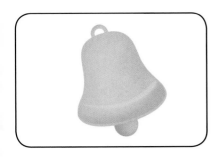 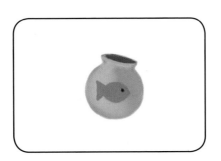 

  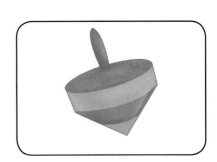

Published in cooperation with Congregational Ministries Publishing,
a ministry of the General Assembly Council, Presbyterian Church (U.S.A.).
ISBN-13: 978-0-8066-6058-5
Manufactured in Canada.
Writer: Debbie Trafton O'Neal
Editors: Cindy Paulson and Timothy W. Larson
Interior design: Michelle L. N. Cook
Cover design: Spunk Design Machine